# The Truth About
# DINOSAURS

D0452708

Dinosaur eggs

| NORTHAMPTONSHIRE LIBRARIES & INFORMATION SERVICES | |
|---|---|
| 60000452327 | |
| Askews & Holts | |
| | |
| BD | |

QUILLS

THE TRUTH ABOUT DINOSAURS

*Het ongelooflijke maar waargebeurde verhaal over de dino's*
First published in Belgium and the Netherlands in 2018
by Clavis Uitgeverij, Hasselt-Amsterdam-New York

This edition published in Great Britain in 2019 by Five Quills
93 Oakwood Court, London W14 8JZ

www.fivequills.co.uk

Five Quills is a trademark of Five Quills

Text and Illustrations copyright © 2018 Clavis Uitgeverij, Hasselt-Amsterdam-New York
English text by Natascha Biebow at Blue Elephant Storyshaping

All rights reserved. No part of this publication may be reproduced,
stored in or introduced to a retrieval system, or transmitted, in any
form or by any means (electronic, mechanical, photocopying, recording
or otherwise), without the prior written permission of the publisher.

A CIP record for this title is available from the British Library

ISBN 978-0-9935537-8-3

1 3 5 7 9 10 8 6 4 2

Printed in Croatia by INK69

# The Truth About
# DINOSAURS

Photo Album

cluck cluck

Guido Van Genechten

EXCUSE ME, BUT I THINK YOU'RE
IN THE WRONG STORY.

Me? No, why? This is my story!

BUT THIS IS A STORY ABOUT DINOSAURS,
AND YOU'RE AN ORDINARY CHICKEN.

What do you mean 'an ordinary chicken'?
Obviously, I'm a dinosaur! Just look at my feet. Real dinosaur feet, right?
Chicken? Humph . . . You mean GALLUS GALLUS DOMESTICUS!

You don't believe me? Wait, I'll get you some proof.

# The Velociraptor Family

Mummy Loci and Daddy Rapt go on a ride together

Little Velo on his new scooter

Here you go! This is our family photo album. I got it from my grandma
(and she got it from her grandma). Look – here are the Velociraptors.
They are my great-great-great-great-great-great-great-great-great-
great-great-great-grand-family. Do you recognize the feet?

75,000,000 BC

Grandpa Raptor takes a stroll

TICKET 13 KG

The Velociraptors had feathers, like me. They couldn't fly,
but they could flap their wings a little like we do.
They were super-fast runners and very clever.

CASA CARA

32

TICKET
4569 KG

Home Sweet Home

HOORAY
FOUR
BABIES

These are the Iguanodons. They are my daddy's distant relatives.
The adults weighed up to 5000 kilos. That's as much as three heavy cars!

125,000,000 BC

A refreshing dip

The family is growing

As you can see, they also laid eggs.

But, um . . . Iguanodon eggs are a bit bigger than mine.

# The Diplodocus Family

Our first diplodo-kiss

Moving day

Here is another side of the family – the Diplodocuses.
They were very big, very tall and very strong . . .
but also very sweet.

150,000,000 BC

On honeymoon

What a view!

TICKET
12,073 KG

A flower
for Dip

MARRIAGE LICENSE

FOR EVER

*Docus and Dip*
are from this day forward together

Docus and Dip can now call themselves Diplodo-KISSES!

Look – two Diplodocuses are kissing under a full moon!
They decided to get married and spend their lives together.
Then they went on a fabulous honeymoon.

Rex

TICKET 8,121 KG

Oh dear, my cousin Tyrannosaurus Rex!
His family were really into roaring, snorting and tearing everything apart.
Look at his gigantic jaws. Each of those sharp teeth was as big as a banana!

65,000,000 BC

Tyra's baby teeth

Backy

Tamtam

Mummy Rex with the little ones

But of course even Tyrannosaurus parents loved their children!

# The Stegosaurus Family

150,000,000 BC

A proud daddy

TICKET 2,014 KG

The Stegosauruses are my favourite relatives. Aren't they great?
We look a lot alike, don't you think?

Stig blows out two candles

My grandpa told me that the Stegosauruses loved to eat plants.
I wonder if they liked corn as much as I do!

# The Triceratops Family

12,700 KG

Lunchtime

A little gas

The Triceratops family also ate lots of plants.
Pee-ew! They were happy, but gassy!

More gas . . .

Something looks wrong

But then, millions of years ago, something went terribly wrong.
Some say the weather got too warm for the dinosaurs.

65,000,000 BC

Asteroid

Earthquake

Others say that a burning-hot asteroid crashed into the Earth.
The Earth trembled, and everything cracked.
Volcanoes spewed out lava and ash into the air.

Volcanic eruptions

The end

The sky turned pitch black, and without sunlight,
the plants died. There was hardly any food left.
In the end, all the dinosaurs starved to death . . .

Well, almost all dinosaurs. Because we, the *Gallus gallus domesticuses*,
are still running around. And we're very proud of our dinosaur feet!
You still don't think these are ordinary chicken feet, do you?

# SO YOU'RE ACTUALLY A DINOSAUR TOO!
# WHAT AN INCREDIBLE STORY.

It might seem incredible, but it's really true.
And now you'll have to excuse me . . .

I have an egg to hatch.

Maybe it will be a cute
little Triceratops.

Or a sweet
Diplodocus . . .

Wait a second . . .

Could it be . . . ?

Four weeks later . . .

Stegosaurus

Diplodocus

Parasuarolophus

Triceratops

Pteranodon

Iguanodon

Gallus gallus domesticus

Anklyosaurus

Tyrannosaurus

Velociraptor